FUSSEL
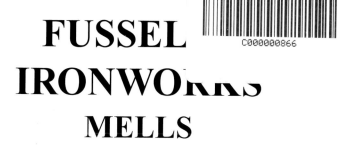

IRONWORKS
MELLS

by
Ken Griffiths and Roy Gallop

A brief history of the Ironworks and family

NEW EDITION

FIDUCIA PRESS

2000

FUSSELLS
IRONWORKS
MELLS

by
Ken Griffiths and Roy Gallop

A brief history
of the Ironworks and family

Typing Services   Leighanne Gough
Photographic Processing   John Brewer
Typography   Ken Griffiths and Roy Gallop
Cover Design   Roy Gallop

First Edition published 1996
Reprinted 1998
New Edition published 2000

Front Cover: Line drawing of an angel carving that once adorned the south west corner of Chantry Church, endowed by James Fussell V. Drawing produced from a photograph taken in the 1930s by Mrs E.L. Green-Armytage.

Title page: William Austin Fussell (1830-1911). His business in Mells supplied wooden handles for edge tools manufactured by other members of the family. A spade-tree manufacturer he also produced garden furniture and horticultural equipment.

Back cover: "Nose to the grindstone". A line drawing depicting a grinder at work. The operator lay full length above the grindstone. This position was not the only method in use. At various times the practice was to straddle or kneel before the grinding wheel.

FIDUCIA PRESS 2000
ISBN 0 946217 07 6
Printed in Great Britain by Doveton Press Ltd., of Bristol.

CONTENTS

FUSSELL'S IRONWORKS MELLS SOMERSET

SITE LAYOUT BASED ON A PLAN C1840-50

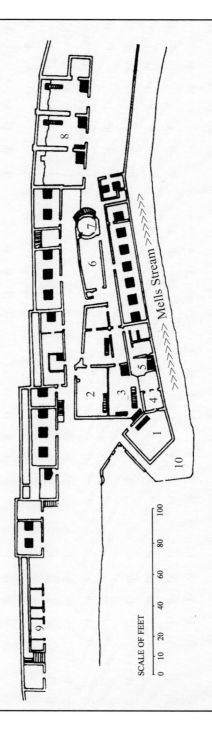

1. & 2. Grinding Shops   3. Tilt Forge   4. Coal House   5. Gas Retort   6. Coal Yard   7. Gasometer   8. Tilt Hammer Shops
9. Stabling   10. Weir

Black Squares represent Forges and Furnaces   Black Rectangles represent Water-wheels

SCALE OF FEET

0 10 20   40   60   80   100

>>>>>> Mells Stream >>>>>>

INTRODUCTION

"This once busy place
Now with verdure overstrewn"

What is now a peaceful river valley once echoed to the clamour of water powered tilt hammers, wreathed in choking smoke from smelting hearths and furnaces.

This site was once described in the eighteenth century as *"looking into the mouth of hell"*. The reference was to the Fussells Ironworks in the Wadbury Valley, near Frome in Somerset, where high quality edge tools were manufactured and exported world wide.

The Fussells enterprise spanned all stages of the Industrial Revolution. This book traces the rise of the Fussell family, the development of the Ironworks and its eventual demise.

The first edition of *"Fussells Ironworks, Mells"* was published in 1996 and reprinted in 1998. Although the main text in this new edition remains largely unaltered, there are now 22 photographs, 10 illustrations, an additional appendix and updated footnotes.

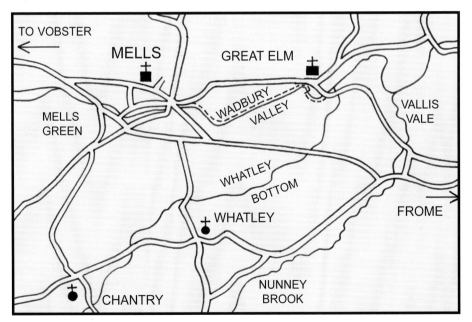

Map of the Mells/Chantry area. There is a public right of way through the Wadbury Valley. However, the site of the Fussells Ironworks is privately owned. Because of the derelict nature of the site the ruins must be considered potentially hazardous.

GETTING IT TOGETHER

I am sure many of us still see the Industrial Revolution on a broad canvas, containing images of dark landscapes, large unhealthy factories, tall chimneys belching soot, and hastily assembled back to back dwelling houses whose inhabitants were considered as much a raw material as coal or iron. This would have been an accurate picture during the later stages of the Industrial Revolution when the systems to ensure maximum efficiency and profits were in place. Our canvas may also contain images of workers meeting to form associations in an attempt to prevent the worst excesses of those systems. The picture comments on the era when Britain was the workshop of the world. Several stages however had to be passed through, involving many factors before this era was reached.

Before the commencement of what was to become an industrialised society, local craftsmen played a major role in the construction of products to serve the needs of a largely agricultural community. Metal tools would be constructed by blacksmiths. There were of course some larger units of production centred on sites with a ready supply of raw materials and availability of water as a power source. They were still on a small scale however and usually served only a limited geographical area. Many factors had to come together before units of production could become larger and more efficient. These factors would include availability of capital, a developing banking system, a developing interest in science, inventions and an expanding overseas market.

During the first half of the eighteenth century all the above-mentioned factors were coming together. Another vital ingredient however was needed before the first stages of the Industrial Revolution could take off, and that was of course an adequate supply of reliable labour.

Since the Civil War there had been a developing trend to enclose the commons. This trend accelerated during the eighteenth century, leaving an increasing number of those dependant on agriculture without the means of subsistence. Deprived of a living from the commons they were obliged to hire their labour for wages. New farming methods and change of land use meant that fewer people were needed to work the land, and many workers could only subsist as casual day labourers. Many agricultural labourers and their families who worked for an estate, and lived in tied cottages with a small amount of land they could work, found themselves 'surplus to requirements'. Eventually this pool of labour provided the workforce necessary to utilise economies of scale and process

Artist Gustave Dore

Contemporary mid-nineteenth century illustration of workers dwellings in London.

working in the new industries. This labour force could also be considered as reliable, as they were vulnerable, wage dependant, and therefore easily exploitable. In areas with the appropriate raw materials and power source (usually water), the combination of all these factors previously mentioned led to the foundation of industrial sites throughout the country. These industries were capable of producing high quality goods in sufficient numbers to reach markets outside their own locality.

Fussells of Mells was just one of many firms that were established in the first phase of the Industrial Revolution. Some of these firms eventually created factories and industries that grew to enormous size, engulfing large areas of the countryside. This in turn led to the growth of new urban areas, initially without basic domestic or social amenities. These industries exported their goods throughout the world, overcoming many difficulties, and gaining the experience that would eventually lead to Britain becoming the world's foremost industrial nation for a considerable period of time.

The very existence of these industrial sites had a profound effect on communications, the transport system being revolutionised. A canal network was established during the first phase of the Industrial Revolution and roads improved. The second phase saw the advent of the railway network. Improved communications had a major influence on the social and economic development of the country.

Fussells Ironworks utilised the factory system, but did not however develop into a large complex, the iron industry being confined to small areas in the region. Nevertheless, the firm was able to compete effectively with larger and more efficient units in other parts of the country. Fussells products were exported world-wide, and the firm survived until the Industrial Revolution was past its peak. This was a remarkable achievement, given the harsh economic philosophy of the period.

We will be discussing how the Fussell family was able to create a business that had an international reputation and sustained it for so long during a period when they did not keep pace with technical advances, unlike the iron industry in the Midlands and North of England.

WHERE IT ALL STARTED

The ruins of Mells Ironworks are set in the Wadbury Valley, cut through by the fast flowing Mells stream. This provided the power source for the foundation site of the Fussell family business. The stream was 'engineered' to ensure that maximum power could be obtained to drive the water-wheels of the factory. Some of the sluice gates can still be seen on the site.

The establishment of the Fussell's first main ironworks followed a long tradition of Mendip ironworking. At one time Mells was also known as Iron Burgh, and this must be an indication of the presence and importance of the craft in this area.

There had in fact been an ironworks in Wadbury Valley before James Fussell III was granted a lease in 1744. The works had been operated by James Naylor, but although derelict by that year were not necessarily in ruins. It is possible that some of the facilities could have been utilised by James Fussell III to assist his early operations.

Fussells Ironworks specialised in the production of agricultural edge tools. As the firm became more successful the ironworks developed its capacity by the expansion of the Mells site and the formation of other ironworks nearby. The ironworks at Mells would have had to accommodate furnaces, forges, bellows, tilt hammers, grindstones, water-wheels and in a later period, rolling mills.

Photo   James Long

A view of Mells Ironworks taken in the early 1880s showing the millpond with the Lower Works behind it.

By the end of the eighteenth century the production techniques and scale of operations were in marked contrast to the more traditional craft practices in the making of iron implements. All the factors mentioned earlier were most obviously in place, and enabled a factory system of production to be achieved.

Photo Carol Griffiths
One of the sluice gates still in existence, at one time controlling the flow of water into the culverts that led to various water-driven machinery.

That the family ironmasters were skilled at developing the factory system cannot be doubted, given the complexity of the workings. Even now, in a ruined state, it is easy to imagine how revolutionary the operation was.

The operations of the ironworks would have generated employment in local and wider areas. Firms directly involved in the production process would include those engaged in the mining and carriage of raw materials and the provision of wooden handles for the agricultural implements. This in turn would promote employment indirectly by the need for road improvements and by the need to service an increased population that occurred around Mells following the success and expansion of the Fussell family business.

One firm that supplied Fussells Ironworks was that of Thomas and Alfred Ashman of Leigh on Mendip. They manufactured wooden handles for the edge tools. In the book *"Victorian and Edwardian Somerset from Old Photographs"** there is a picture of Ashman's timber yard. It is not only an interesting photograph, but also poignant as it was taken in the year the Mells Ironworks closed. One can imagine the effect this had on the Ashman business.

In 1975 the Bristol Industrial Archaeological Society published an account in their *"Journal"*** of a survey they undertook on the Mells site in 1974/5. This edition contains a site layout based on a plan of the Ironworks in the mid-nineteenth century and gives a good indication of the factory's processes in that period.

The Ironworks as they exist today can best be described as a double ribbon of ruined structures at different levels. Each structure provided in its day a different but integral function in the production process, although today it is difficult to identify the functions of some of these structures.

SETTING THE STANDARD

It would be interesting to have access to the business papers relating to the Fussell Ironworks. Unfortunately none have come to light, and it must be feared that they are irretrievably lost or destroyed.

There are however other documents relating to the Fussell family and the ironworks. Research by Robin Atthill enabled him to state that among the Horner papers preserved at Mells Manor was a document dated the 25th December 1744, by which John Horner leased a plot of ground to James Fussell of Stoke Lane, Edge-Toolmaker, for 99 years with liberty to erect...

> *"a good, firme and substantial Mill or Mills for Grinding Edge Tools and forging Iron plates".*

It will be noted that in this document James Fussell is already described as an

---

*   Introduction and Commentaries by David Bromwich and Robert Dunning.

**   It is our understanding that the Bristol Industrial Archaeological Society may publish all the information they hold on the site at some future date. It is also likely that a new site map will be included.

Photo John Cornwell

Surveying the culverts at the Fussells site in the Wadbury Valley during the archaeological dig in the 1970s. Although out of sight these culverts were the vital arteries that carried water to drive the water-wheels. Even after many years of neglect it is possible to see the high standard of masonry depicted in this dramatic photograph.

edge tool maker. The likelihood is that he was already engaged in the trade in a small way, and may very well have been a craftsman with the necessary capital to set himself up as an ironmaster. In the absence of any records associated with the Fussell business we can only speculate how James Fussell raised the finance to start such an enterprise. It is known that the Fussell family were established in the area by 1646, and this stability of background, together with craft skills could have been of interest to one of the emerging banks wishing to invest in likely profitable enterprises. We have no way of course of being certain of this, but many other enterprises around the country were started in this way at about the same time.

Having secured land and capital James Fussell would have been able to find the labour for his enterprise from the growing pool of landless, wage dependant workers. James Fussell had therefore the means of production.

As mentioned earlier, the founder of Mells Ironworks came from a locally established family. He was in fact known as James Fussell III, being descended from Thomas Fussell, whose son James Fussell I was born at Stoke Lane in 1646. The Fussell family had many branches and gradually spread over a larger area in Somerset and into Wiltshire. As Robin Atthill states...

"James Fussell III may be regarded as the founder not only of the business, but also of the Mells branch of the family."

We will be largely discussing this branch of the family, but if the reader is interested in the extended Fussell family a very well researched account can be found in Robin Atthill's book *"Old Mendip"*.

Eventually branches of the Fussell family were operating six ironworks in the area. Two were situated in Mells, the foundation site, these being called the Upper Works and Lower Works. The other ironworks were situated at Great Elm, Railford, Chantry and Nunney. The three sons of the founder, Austin Fussell (1737-1794), John Fussell I (1740-1821) and James Fussell IV (1748-

Photo James Long

Another 1880s view of the Mells Ironworks clearly showing the cramped nature of the site during it's final developmental stage. The Mells Stream flowed closely behind the left hand rake of buildings. By this time steam power had been used for approximately twenty years.

1832) all took an active part in the business.

It is evident that James Fussell's venture was successful from the beginning, his products from the ironworks being of such proven quality that by the end of the century they were being exported to Europe and the Americas. There is a reference to this in John Collinson's *"The History and Antiquities of Somerset (1791)"*.

"it is worthy of remark that in the sequestered vale there are two iron forges which at this period are carrying on a trade, little inferior, in point of extension, to those in the northern part of this Kingdom. All the western counties are supplied at these manufactories with every iron implement of husbandry, and their connections extend to the European and American continents."

The reputation gained by Fussells of Mells for the production of fine quality agricultural tools appears to have continued throughout the life of the business, extending from the eighteenth century to the approach of the twentieth. This has been confirmed by our own studies. For example, an examination of Kelly's *'Directory of Somerset'* will reveal entries in 1866, 1872, 1883, 1889 and 1894, which describe two factories operated by Fussells of Mells as being for the...

"manufacture of agricultural edge-tools, which have long been celebrated for their superior quality."

An entry in Morris' *Directory* for 1871 gives, together with the names of the various branches of the family business, examples of the type of products produced by their factories...

> *James Fussell Sons & Co - Mells Ironworks*
> *(Sythes, bagging and reaping hooks, hay and chaff knives)*
>
> *John Fussell & Co - Upper Ironworks*
> *(Spade shovel & edge tool manufacturers)*
>
> *William A Fussell - Rock House*
> *(Spade & shovel tree manufacturer)*
>
> *Isaac Fussell & Co of Nunney*
> *(Spade, shovel & edge-tool manufacturers)*

From the Somerset Archaeological Society's collection.

Thomas and Alfred Ashman's timber yard. This firm at Leigh on Mendip made handles for the edge tools manufactured by Fussells Ironworks. A poignant photograph as it may have been taken around the time the ironworks closed in 1895.

Robin Atthill quotes from the *"Bristol Journal"* of the 6th August 1803, and further quotes an editorial comment from the same paper published one hundred years later. These two quotes give a very good indication not only of the reputation enjoyed by Fussells of Mells, but also of the high production capable of being achieved by the ironworks in 1803. The first quote from the *"Bristol Journal"* of the 6th August 1803 relates to the very serious invasion threat from France during this period.

"At this eventful and momentous crisis, when the heart of every Briton beats high with true loyalty and patriotism, we feel pleasure in recording the spirited offers made to Government for the defence of the country. Mr James Fussell, of the Mells Iron Factory, near Frome, has offered to prepare (gratis) 1,000 pikes, and afterwards to supply Government with 2,000 weekly as long as they may be wanted."

The editorial quote, one hundred years later begins...

"Good old patriotic James Fussell! When I was a lad, your name was still a household word in the district for bill hooks, reaping-tools, etc, and my grand-father had tools of your make he set great store by. It may be so still, or that of your Successors, so far as I know, if the cheaper but not better Sheffield tools have not overrun the market. I will warrant your Somerset pikes would have rendered good service in the hands of Somerset men had it come to the push, and the West Country men had not been bundled between the rhines, where they could not come at their foes, as they were at Sedgemoor."

The Rev. John Skinner, the rector of Camerton, made a visit to one of the iron-works on the 15th July 1828. The following is an extract from his diary for that day...

"I rose before seven, and walked with Richard Hoare to the Iron Works at Nunney to purchase a scythe for mowing the garden, as the best in the country, perhaps in the kingdom, are made by the Fussells, who have mills at Mells, Nunney and Little Elm, and have realised an immense property among the fra-ternity by their superior skills in hardening edged tools..."

During a visit we made to Chantry Church, whose foundation will be discussed later, we met Mr Charles George, a retired quarryman who, using woodwork skills, was restoring the rood screen. He also gave a testimonial to the fine quality of Fussells tools, stating that good examples are still in use. His family has been resident in the area over several generations. Interestingly he also mentioned that one of the best tools he had ever used was made by a blacksmith. As mentioned earlier James Fussell III also had such craft origins.

Roy, who was born and raised in Somerset, can recall his grandfather owning, and extensively using Fussells tools, having a life-long interest in gardening.

During a visit we made to Frome Museum we saw a very fine example of a Fussell Single Hand Axe, a sturdy business-like tool, and one could see why such tools as this had such a good reputation and were in such great demand.

We were also fortunate enough to be able to see and handle many Fussells edge tools that have been used over several generations. Their owners assured us that they still give sterling service.

The above accounts are testimonials to the good quality of Fussells implements.

It should be remembered however that shortly before the closure of the Ironworks in 1895 the good will of the business was aquired by Isaac Nash of Worcestershire. This firm, when manufacturing edge tools in the West Midlands, from Fussells designs and techniques, continued to use the Fussells trademarks. Therefore not all edge tools with Fussells trademarks are necessarily Somerset products.

A CUT ABOVE THE REST

What made these tools so special that they were described as being of superior quality over many generations? Several reasons come to mind. The founder of the ironworks was a craftsman himself, and personally supervised production during the foundation period. He would have passed his skills on to the newly employed workforce, and insisted on the highest of standards.

Quality control was obviously good, the business being small enough even at the end of the nineteenth century to make this possible. Although eventually there were six ironworks operated by various branches of the Fussell family, none of these developed into large mass production units that were a feature of the later stages of the Industrial Revolution. This meant of course that although division of labour must have been a feature of the Fussell operations, there was still scope for the use of craft skills in some of the processes. A measure of job satisfaction was therefore possible enabling some of the workers to achieve some

*The end product, a bill-hook, handle not original, stamped **"Fussells Improved".** Tool loaned by Mr William Council for an on site photograph.*

dignity from their labours.

Another reason why Fussells tools were of superior quality could have been the possibility that there was a continuity in the labour force. Workers probably stayed with the firm all their working lives, having no choice in many instances. Members of the same family could have served Fussells over many generations. This continuity of labour could have built into the operation a considerable fund of skilled knowledge, which of course would directly influence the quality of the products.

In an article by Dr. R. D. Reid in the *'Somerset Year Book 1935',* he comments on a fascinating reason why Fussells tools had the edge on others.
He states...

"Mr Fussell apparently did his own smelting and it is said that he mixed the black oxide of manganese (fairly common on Mendip) with the iron ore, and that gave a peculiar virtue to his iron. If so, he seems to have discovered the modern manganese steel alloy in very early days"

If the Mr Fussell referred to by Dr. Reid was the founder of the Mells Ironworks it could account for the firm's swift success.

It is possible that all these factors had a part to play in ensuring the high esteem in which Fussells tools were held.

ROAD, RAIL, NO CANAL

James Fussell IV obviously saw the advantages that an improved transport system would bring to the business. Not only did he promote the Dorset and Somerset Canal Scheme, he designed a patent Balance Lock (Canal Lift). This Balance Lock was not only built but proved to be of sound design, having been demonstrated successfully in 1800. The Dorset and Somerset Canal was intended to link the Bristol and English Channels. This aim was to be achieved by the construction of a canal from Bath to Poole. Mells would have been served by a

Photo John Brewer

Murtry Aquaduct near Frome carried the Dorset and Somerset Canal over the Mells River. This section of the canal actually became operational for a short time before the whole scheme was abandoned. Built nearly two hundred years ago the quality, grandeur of the design and construction is a sure indication that the promoters of the scheme, of whom James Fussell IV was one, were firm in their intention in linking the Bristol and English Channels. Only lack of capital prevented this. This structure would not look out of place in classical Bath.

branch from Frome. However, the required capital was not forthcoming and the Scheme was abandoned. The project however does demonstrate the inventiveness, sometimes flair, of the proprietors of industries in that period. Of course they were very well acquainted and involved in the endeavours they ran, being familiar with all the processes and being quite capable of applying their minds to ensure technical advances.

James Fussell IV must have been acutely disappointed at the failure of the Canal Scheme. As we know from contemporary reports road conditions in Britain in the mid-eighteenth century were poor. They were often impassable in the winter. Barely adequate to suit local needs, these roads could not meet the demands made on them by the growing industries, searching for, and securing larger markets.

Photo John Brewer

Packhorse bridge at Edford, built two hundred years ago to carry the drove road over the working section of the Dorset and Somerset Canal. This road was used to transport coal from the pits at Stratton Common.

Road transport was improved to meet these new demands by the creation of Turnpike Trusts. These organisations filled the gap between the coming of the railways and the involvement of central and local government in road planning, building and maintenance.

James Fussell III would have experienced transport difficulties during the first few years of his business, but relief arrived with the establishment of the Turnpike Trust in the area during the 1750s. The Trusts spread and linked up to form a network, bringing trading benefits to Fussells and others. Fifty years later however his son was still looking for a more efficient method of transport that could cut costs. The abandonment of the Canal Scheme made it even more important that the road network became more efficient.

1815 saw the appointment of John Loudon McAdam as Surveyor General of the Bristol Road Trusts. His road construction methods were revolutionary and cost effective. Gradually John McAdam's methods spread throughout the country (although modified later to include the ideas of another road engineer, Thomas Telford).

By 1825 the Bristol Trusts operated nearly 70 miles of roads in Somerset, all of sound construction. It must be noted however that the condition of the minor roads would still have been poor.

Fussells must have benefited by these road extensions, but nevertheless a canal would have complemented these new transport improvements.

The abandonment of the Dorset and Somerset Canal was also a loss to us. Even if built it would of course have eventually closed and suffered a period of neglect; but it would, in the light of other canal restoration experience, have been re-opened, to local economic advantage and to the social advantage of us all.

The Wiltshire, Somerset and Weymouth Railway brought the railway to Frome in 1850, the same year as the company was absorbed by the Great Western Railway. A branch to Radstock from Frome was opened in 1854.

The main line was further extended, until in 1857 it passed through Dorset to reach Weymouth.

Photo Carol Griffiths

The courtyard of the Talbot Inn, Mells.
This inn hosted some of the first meetings to discuss
the Dorset and Somerset Canal Scheme.

Undoubtedly Fussells used the services this new transport facility could pro-vide. As the railway network gradually spread throughout the region the Fussell family would have, at last, an efficient transport system available to favour their business.

Interestingly the main line of the Wiltshire, Somerset and Weymouth Railway, the first in East Mendip, has survived, whereas the lines of later arrivals are now silent. The East Somerset, the Bristol and North East Somerset, and the Somerset and Dorset Railways survived absorption, amalgamation and nation-alisation, but unfortunately they could not survive 'rationalisation'.*

THE FAMILY MAKES IT'S MARK

James Fussell IV lived a long and active life. Of his eight children, five were sons. It appears that all his sons were actively involved in the family business. However, the youngest son, Jacob, eventually took Holy Orders becoming the Vicar of Doulting. It is clear that the Fussells had become well advanced in the community at this stage of the family history. The eldest son, James Fussell V built himself a mansion at Chantry and later built and endowed a church in the grounds. Although the endowment of the church could be seen as further secur-ing the Fussells' social position, it does seem likely that a new church was nec-essary. It is known that there was an increase in population in the vicinity of the ironworks, and it would seem appropriate to form a new parish from parts of Whatley, Mells and Elm.

Although James Fussell V died the year before the consecration of the new parish church, he would have been able to see the almost completed building from his mansion.

Chantry Church was consecrated by the Bishop of Bath and Wells on the 4th June 1846. The Rev. J.H.S. Horner (Rector of Mells) and the Rev. Jacob Fussell (Vicar of Doulting) assisted in the service, together with James Fussell VI who was to be the first Vicar of Chantry. He was the nephew and heir of James Fussell V.

* Part of the East Somerset line is preserved at Cranmore, and has access to the main railway network. One of the aims of another Railway Preservation Society, The North Somerset Trust and Railway is the restoration of the Frome to Radstock connection.

The presence of a member of the Horner family in the company of a member of the Fussell family, who was the Vicar of the new church must be seen as significant. They would both be seen by the community as of equal social status. At the time of the consecration of the church the Horners had been Lords of the Manor since the Reformation, receiving the title deeds at the time of the Dissolution. (The nursery rhyme Little Jack Horner may refer to this, the plum being the title deeds. Please see Appendix 1).

It would not have been seen as unusual for a member of the Horner family to hold a position within the Church and be present at such an occasion. But also present in positions of equality and authority were two members of a family descended from a craftsman.

Photo Carol Griffiths

Chantry Church, built and endowed by James Fussell V. Consecrated by the Bishop of Bath and Wells on the 4th of June 1846. Designed in the Gothic revival style, the interior presents an almost non-conformist functional appearance, in contrast to what was once a more decorated and flamboyant exterior.

Although the Fussells social advancement had accelerated during the life of James Fussell V, the ritual of consecration could be said to have proved to the Horners and the community that a new squirearchy had been established. Carvings of angels, some holding edge tools adorned the outside of the church, leaving no doubt as to the origin of the endowment.

The angel carvings have been seriously eroded over the years, but one angel, albeit headless, can still be seen carrying a reaphook. On the south west corner of the church, above the buttress, one can just make out the fragile remains of an angel wing, all that is left of a once fine figure.

Fortunately there is a photograph of this particular angel in its complete state in *"Old Mendip"*, taken by Mrs E.L. Green-Armytage.

Photo Carol Griffiths

Chantry House. Pre-dating Chantry Church it was built by James Fussell V as his mansion. Constructed in a rather severe Classical style it is no longer occupied by any member of the Fussell family.

Roy, by careful examination of this photograph, has been able to produce a drawing of the figure to enhance the detail. Although, as stated, the angel carving no longer graces the church, we hope that we have given it a new lease of life by placing the image on the front cover of this book.

It is well worth a visit to Chantry Church. From the churchyard one has a clear view of Chantry House, no longer occupied by any member of the Fussell family.

A memorial tablet to some members of the Fussell family, including the founder of the ironworks, can be found in the Mells Parish Church of St Andrews. This church too is worthy of a visit. A very informative leaflet can be found within the church, and reveals the association of the parish with political, literary and artistic figures.

Also in Mells is the Talbot Inn, where some of the first meetings were held to discuss the Dorset and Somerset Canal Scheme.

We have already commented on the increase of population that took place in the years following the foundation of the ironworks. Ten years after the consecration of Chantry Church a school was erected in the parish. At this time James Fussell VI was H.M. Inspector of Schools and although he was based in London it was likely that he was influential in the founding of the school. Robin Atthill says that this was a unique comprehensive school. An examination of the educational structure certainly confirms this.

In Kelly's *"Directory of Somerset(1861)"* there is an entry...

"National, Industrial and Boarding School (for girls), Miss S S Kyberd, Principal"

All these functions were carried out under the same roof and an infant class was also accommodated within the complex. The Industrial School was for girls, who although trained in domestic tasks, were also, according to a report by the Board of Education in 1860, given instruction in geography, reading, writing and arithmetic. The report also states that...

"It is impossible to visit the institution without feeling that no care and expense are spared in making the school efficient and the young persons happy."

The function of the boarding school was to train girls to become governesses and teachers. An entry in Kelly's *"Directory of Somerset (1875)"* describes the function of the school...

"To bring within the reach of persons with limited income the benefits of a good education, including French, German, Music, Drawing, and such other accomplishments as are usually imprinted in schools of superior character."

Mary Fussell, the daughter of James Fussell VI, was at one time the Headmistress of Chantry School, *"for many years"*, according to Robin Atthill.

Bearing in mind that the schools were set up before the passing of the 1870 Education Act, it does seem that certain features of Chantry School were ahead of their time. This Education Act of course was very important, as it secured local finance in education, and no child developed into adulthood without an elementary education, the poor being excused fees. In Kelly's *"Directory of Somerset (1910)"* no mention is made of the National, Industrial or Boarding Schools. The previous entries have been replaced with *"Public Elementary School (mixed)"*.

Robin Atthill states...
"there is an amusing picture of Chantry School in the once popular, and now almost forgotten novel "Comin' thro' the Rye", which was published in 1875."

The author, Helen Mathers, was a pupil at the school, which in the novel is disguised as "Charteris". James Fussell VI is described in the book as Mr Russell.

The novel is still recalled by Mr George. He was born in the Boarding School section of Chantry School when it had ceased to provide that function, his mother being the Caretaker of the Church Elementary School that functioned within the former comprehensive complex.

He informed us that *"Comin' thro' the Rye"* would give a good account of life in the school during the nineteenth century, so it is evident that there is still a community memory being preserved of a different era and way of life.*

* A reference copy of *"Comin' thro' the Rye"* is held at the Somerset Studies Library, Taunton. Lending copies are available at Yeovil and Frome Libraries and at Bristol Central Library.

WHAT ABOUT THE WORKERS ?

During the nineteenth century the term "Captains of Industry" was often used. The term of course referred to industrialists who organised their business on almost military lines, and were often single minded and aggressive in order to achieve their aims. But as in the military where the organisation could not function without the rank and file, the industrial organisations could not function without the labouring classes. It would be interesting and just if it were possible to trace the history of a family whose members had worked for Fussells over several generations. It is most unlikely if such a first hand account exists, given the limited educational facilities available to workers and their children during much of the period under discussion, and of course limited leisure time.

However, there is a wealth of contemporary information available to give an accurate, though general picture of the sort of lives workers would have led during the Industrial Revolution.

The various Factory Acts implemented throughout the nineteenth century must give an indication that those with privileges and vested interests considered workers, even child workers, as just the labour factor in the production process. A general picture emerges of the labour force only securing even basic human rights by the means of legislation after agitation. There were of course exceptions, some proprietors of industrial concerns adopting not just liberal and sensible regimes, but experimented with alternative economic systems, for example Co-operatives.

To the surprise of many the shortening of hours actually led to increased production, but legislation was still necessary to compel the "Captains of Industry" to have regard for their workers welfare. Llewellyn Woodward in his book *"The Age of Reform"* comments on the effects of the 1850 Factory Act, limiting the number of hours that could be worked by women and young persons...

"The results of shortening the hours of labour justified those who foretold that there would be little or no falling off in production. The fall was slight even when machinery was run at the old speeds, and in most cases the operatives were so much healthier in mind and body that they could stand the strain of working with the machines at higher speeds."

The operatives referred to above would have been working in the cotton and woollen industries, where the factory system was well advanced in certain areas of the country, but the effect on the morale of the workers in other industries by a betterment of conditions also improved production and the quality of the end product. In spite of growing evidence to this effect employers of labour still resisted almost every move to treat their workers as they would wish to be treated themselves.

My grandfather, who was a craftsman, imparted to me his view that...

"If an employer was as careful with his workers as a craftsman was with his tools, business would be better, and the world a better place."

It would be pleasing to imagine that the Fussell family throughout the operation of the business were liberal and sensible employers. It is likely that the first

Workers Collage.
A portrayal of the many unacknowledged workers who provided the muscle and skill during the Industrial Revolution.

group of workers employed by James Fussell III in the mid-eighteenth century were vulnerable and easily exploitable. The workforce probably remained vulnerable throughout the life of the business. This is not to say that the Fussells took advantage of this and engaged in heavy exploitation. We know for example that another institution in the area, the Chantry School, was quite enlightened for the age. But even this does not indicate that all the educational facilities were open to the poor or even to the factory workers children.

Given that Jacob Fussell, James Fussell VI and John T R Fussell were Church Ministers, the last two mentioned being owners of the ironworks in the area, one would hope that during their tenure they would have seen the welfare of their workers as a priority.

In an earlier period however it was remarked by the Rev. John Skinner in 1828 that the condition of the workers could be likened to bondage. To quote further from his diary entry for the 15th July 1828, he records that...

"We saw two men grinding scythes, with their noses literally to the grindstone; if any of our West Indian slaves had been seen by any of our modern philanthropists in such a situation, the tocsin of anti-servial malediction would have resounded from John of Groats' house to the Lands' End. Oh! Ye Liberals and ye soi-distant Philanthropists! Ye strain at a gnat and swallow a camel; ye confine the people in bonds more heavy to be borne than any the most cruel of Indian planters ever imposed on their property."

Robin Atthill also comments, obviously through research, that the Fussells had a reputation of being hard taskmasters. Interestingly, during our conversation with Mr George he volunteered the information that inherited family memory indicated that the Fussells were not the most enlightened of employers.

Robin Atthill relates that...
"There is a story of rioting in Chantry against the Fussells, over the question of the eviction of some cottagers from houses required for their workers."

Reference to rioting in Chantry was also referred to by Mr George.

Presumably conditions improved gradually with the implementation of the various Factory Acts passed throughout the nineteenth century.

END OF THE ROAD

We have then a picture of a thriving business with a reputation for good quality products. By the end of the nineteenth century however all production at the ironworks had ceased.

How was it that such a long established and powerful family business came to an end?
Like some past civilisation or empire that must have seemed indestructible for countless number of years, Fussells Ironworks finally succumbed. But to what? Even powerful dynasties can sometimes fragment and fade into memory, but there is rarely a simple or single reason to account for this happening.

Under the Mells section of Kelly's *"Directory of Somerset (1883)"* the ironworks are listed as...

"Fussell James, Isaac and John <u>Limited,</u> bar iron steel - edge tool manufacturer and at Nunney, Elm and Chantry."

A manager is listed for the first time. Further managers were listed in the editions of 1889 and 1894. This could indicate that the personal involvement of the Fussell family had diminished to a 'lack of interest' level. According to Robin Atthill all production had ceased by 1895. By that time the business was in the hands of a Worcestershire firm, Isaac Nash. Certainly we know that there was no listing of the ironworks in the 1897 edition of Kelly's *"Directory."*

It is likely that there was a slow decline in the fortunes of the business since the agricultural slump of the 1870s. Not only would this have decreased the demand for agricultural implements but buyers still in the market would have sought cheaper alternatives, readily available from the Midlands and North of England, where larger and more efficient production units had been established.

We have already discussed the fine products produced by Fussells Ironworks, the purchase of which could be looked on as a long-term investment. In the economic climate at the time of the agriculture slump however the short-term gain from buying cheaper, though inferior tools would take priority over other considerations.
It is also evident that Fussells, in common with many firms that were estab-

Photo Marchant Jones

The Mells Ironworks closed in 1895. This stark picture, taken around the time of the First World War well illustrates the desolation and swift decay that took place. The three arches in the lower level of the rake of buildings still survive, although the upper levels are now missing. (See picture below). During the past two decades the decline in this country's manufacturing base has once again led to scenes of roofless factories becoming commonplace. Sadly, this decline still continues.

Photo Carol Griffiths

A recent photograph of the Hammer Sheds on the Mells site. Even in this late stage of decay one can see the fine masonry arches that once supported two further levels. (See above).

lished at the dawn of the Industrial Revolution, were slow in keeping pace with new technology after the first advances. For example, water was the power source in the Fussells Ironworks for the greater part of their operating life. Steam was introduced eventually but did not lead to any extensive expansion of the sites. Such expansion could have led to the economies of scale necessary to compete effectively in the market. But for this to happen it would have also been vital for the owners at the time to have had the original drive, expertise and commitment of previous ironmasters.

James Fussell VI and his brother, John T.R. Fussell, would have been the owners at the time steam was introduced. It is doubtful that either possessed the qualities mentioned, both pursuing careers independent of the business. This was a common enough feature among third or fourth generations within a dynasty that had humble origins. Increasing wealth led to each succeeding generation receiving superior education and to an improvement in their social status. Family income from the business would not necessarily be ploughed back, and in many instances invested elsewhere. This would enrich the family, but could only lead to a decline of the foundation business, to the detriment of the workers and the community who had sustained the fortunes of the dynasty. It could very well be that the Fussell family fell into this category. There had been a growing trend amongst the extended Fussell family to live and work away from Somerset, thereby isolating themselves from the community.

All of the above points may have created the conditions where a take-over could take place. It is possible that the firm of Isaac Nash was more interested in acquiring the goodwill element of the business rather than investing in the ironworks. We know that near the time of closure Fussells could produce 111 types of tool, each capable of being modified by request to suit the needs of the purchaser. After the Somerset Ironworks closed the Nash factory in Worcestershire used the Fussells trademark when these tools were produced there.

As a result of our wandering through the ruins of the ironworks at Mells, we often indulged in imaginings as to whether the history of Fussells Ironworks could have had a different outcome.

The influence of capitalism runs as a continuous thread throughout the period that the ironworks operated. There were of course alternative economic systems being advocated at the time, but these were resisted by those with financial and political power. A more rapid extension of the franchise would have been necessary if any change of economic system was to have any chance of success. This we know did not happen, Britain's efforts at democracy being laborious at best. Democracy then came too late for any serious challenge to capitalism, the system and its myths being too well established.

Without going into detail, those advocating alternative economic systems held certain common views, namely that the aim of any economic system is the com-

Photo John Cornwell

One of the volunteers on the 1970s dig. The work of excavating, often a mixture of heavy labour and skilful attention to detail, revealed information on the site's long history of industrial occupation.

mon good. They believed that economic competition led to conflict, even war, and was therefore damaging to the human condition. They saw that competition was a contradiction within the system that advocated it, competition being suppressed by those initially favoured by it whenever an opportunity arose to improve their economic position. The take-over of Fussells was an example of this. There are modern examples also.

Would Fussells have survived into the twentieth century if capitalism as an economic system been replaced in the nineteenth century by the co-operative sys-

The Fussells Ironworks site at Mells during the excavation by the Bristol Industrial Archaeological Society in the 1970s. To the left of the picture Mells Stream pours through the breach in the mill pond dam. A more recent picture of what is left of the arched tilt hammer sheds can be seen on page 31. Unfortunately the site was not protected, thereby depriving the community of a rich slice of visual industrial history.

tem, as advocated and practised by Robert Owen (1771-1858)? Even considering this is somewhat fanciful, but let us assume that a change did take place.

Certainly the workers environment would have changed for the better under the new system, and this would have had beneficial effects on the wider community. An argument has been advanced that if the co-operative system had become as widespread as capitalism, factories would have been part of a countrywide trading system, the ethos of which would be the promotion of a fair distribution of goods and services. It would not have been necessary to adhere to capitalist principles that had been developing since the Civil War, and recorded as a body of knowledge by Adam Smith and others in the eighteenth century. Free of the burden of competition, the economy could be <u>planned</u> for the well being of Society. No one person would have a gross abundance of wealth over another.

It is likely that under a planned economy the Fussells Ironworks would have performed a vital role within this trading system. Of course, the nation's institutions would have had to be the subject of major change for this system to work.

It is possible then that Fussells would have survived within a different economic system, maybe even for a longer period; smaller perhaps, radically re-organised certainly, but still producing traditionally crafted and superior products.

Photo Carol Griffiths
A supervised activity in the quiet and once again beautiful Wadbury valley.

LAST WORDS

None of the six ironworks developed into the very large units that were a feature of the later stages of the Industrial Revolution.

In this respect the communities around Mells were spared the de-spoiling of their countryside and way of life. The area within Buckland Dinham to the North, Nunney to the South, Frome to the East and Mells to the West, is of outstanding natural beauty.

A walk through the Wadbury Valley will soon bring contact with the ruins of the ironworks. They are small enough not to intrude on the beautiful aspect, but substantial enough to be quietly stimulating. Thankfully the area under discussion has been preserved from the worst ravages of a harsh economic system, and it would be only just, in our view, that the ruins should be preserved also. Visual history is always exciting, particularly to the young. Many economic and social lessons could be learned from the past, to the benefit of future generations, but sadly, even if learnt, are often ignored.

An interest in local history is often the first step towards a community understanding of the need to be watchful in the protection of the environment and peoples.

There is a growing awareness today of the link between a pleasant, peaceful environment and the quality of life, the real 'feel good factor.' We can be thankful that in place of the bleakness of a post-industrial environment, which so easily could have been the case in this part of Somerset, we have a sylvan scene that delights the eye and gladdens the heart.

"APPENDIX 1

Little Jack Horner

Little Jack Horner
Sat in a corner,
Eating his Christmas pie.
He put in his thumb
And pulled out a plum,
And said, "What a good boy am I!".

There have been disputes as to whether or not the nursery rhyme referred to an ancestor of the Horner family. It has been suggested that it can be traced to 1767 when the rhyme appeared in a popular comical story in verse *"The History of Jack Horner"*. There are, however, earlier references, and it is likely that the rhyme has a long history, being included in stories and ballads because of its popularity and its allusion to opportunism.

As recorded in the *"Oxford Dictionary of Nursery Rhymes"*... *"from the historical angle, there is no objection to the short rhyme having originally referred to the Horner ancestor."*

Thomas Horner, a steward to Abbot Richard Whyting of Glastonbury Abbey, purchased several manors in Somerset following the confiscation of the abbey holdings by Henry VIII.

The *"Oxford Dictionary of Nursery Rhymes"* continues...

"Glastonbury, at the beginning of 1539, was the only religious house in Somerset left untouched, and it was the richest abbey in the kingdom. When Abbot Whyting was on trial for his life, Thomas Horner was a member of the complaisant jury which condemned him. It is admitted that Horner benefited by being a King's man, and the local people may well have had their own ideas about how he acquired his estates. A couplet, still current in Somersetshire, which was put on record as early as 1680 runs...

"Hopton, Horner, Smyth, Thynne,
When abbots went out, they came in".

Abbot Whyting was dragged on a hurdle to the summit of Glastonbury Tor, and there executed. The aged abbot had a reputation as a saintly man and one can imagine the feelings of local people and others at this crime, one of the most ruthless and unnecessary acts ever sanctioned by Henry VIII.

Another member of the Horner family, John of Cloford, took up residence in Mells, and so began the long association of his descendants with the area.

It is tempting to link John Horner with the Jack Horner of the nursery rhyme, Jack often being substituted for John. It is more likely however that the rhyme refers to the bachelor Thomas Horner, a member of the jury disposed to comply with the King's wishes, with tragic results.

If the nursery rhyme does refer to Thomas Horner, why Jack?

This could have been a deliberate change of name by the author, Jack being another word for knave. 'Jack the Lad' is still in current use to describe someone with a eye to the main chance.

The nursery rhyme could very well have come about as a safe, effective way of making peoples feelings of outrage known at the time. After all we know that ballads were often used as a medium of protest when other channels were closed or forbidden.

The fact that Thomas Horner served on the jury that condemned Richard Whyting, and became the Lord of several manors' following the Crown seizure of Church lands, could have led to understandable suspicions that he was favoured in their purchase, hence, possibly, the nursery rhyme.

Photo Peter Gallop

Glastonbury Tor, Somerset.

APPENDIX 2

Finch Brothers' Foundry
(Sticklepath Museum of Rural Industry)

A present day visitor to the Fussells foundation site in the Wadbury Valley would find it difficult to envisage the various stages of production in the making of edge tools that were once produced in this manufactory in such large quantities.

Readers who have an interest in how the tools were made, and the type of machinery used by the workshops are recommended to make a visit to the Sticklepath Museum of Rural Industry, Sticklepath, near Okehampton, Devon. This working museum has water driven machinery similar to that once installed at Fussells Ironworks.

Although the Finch Brothers' Foundry operated throughout its existence on a much smaller scale than Fussells Ironworks, nonetheless, a visit to Sticklepath will offer the opportunity to see how edge tools were made and finished.

Finch Foundry was established in 1814 by William Finch, a blacksmith. It remained a family business throughout its operational life. From 1945 the Foundry operated under the name of Finch Brothers Ltd., the directors being Ralph Finch, Charles Bowden and Richard Barron. The firm ceased trading in 1960, but thanks largely to the commitment and vision of the late Richard (Dick) Barron, the grandson of Albany George Finch (1864-1945), this small factory has been saved to form part of our industrial heritage.

The museum, once administered by the Finch Foundry Trust has now passed into the capable hands of the National Trust.

Included in this Appendix are photographs taken at the Foundry.

One of the three large water-wheels that provide the motive power for the various operations within the manufactory. All three wheels are overshot, water being fed from above by a wooden launder, easily accessible to the visitor.

Photo   Carol Griffiths

Jim Coyne demonstrating the steeling hammer, the lighter of the two tilt hammers. This hammer has a striking rate of about 240 blows per minute. In the background is the much heavier plating hammer that can strike 180 blows per minute.

Photo   Carol Griffiths

A small selection of the many types of edge tools once produced commercially at the Finch Brothers' Foundry. The firm also produced a large number of shovels and other hand tools for use in the Devon and Cornwall copper, tin and china clay industries.

Photos in this display, courtesy of the Museum of Dartmoor Life, Okehampton, and Museum of English Rural Life, Reading.

Photo Carol Griffiths

Another process being demonstrated by Jim Coyne. The cast iron shears were used to cut red hot steel bar into the appropriate lengths for the various edge tools. The shears, together with the tilt hammers share the same axle rotated by the large water-wheel.

Acknowledgements

Copyright material has been used from the following publications:

"Old Mendip" by Robin Atthill (David and Charles 1964) by kind permission of the publishers; "The Age of Reform 1815-1870" by Llewellyn Woodward (Oxford University Press 1992); "The Oxford Dictionary of Nursery Rhymes" edited by Ian P Opie (Oxford University Press 1992) by kind permission of the publishers; "The Journal of a Somerset Rector 1803 - 1834" edited by Howard and Peter Coombes (Kingsmead Press 1987) by kind permission of the publishers. Reproductions from "Woodcuts by Thomas Bewick and his School" (Edited by Blanche Cirker, published by Dover Publications Inc. New York 1962). Photograph of Ashman's timber yard by kind permission of the Somerset Archaeological and Natural History Society. Photograph of William Austin Fussell reproduced from "Old Mendip" by Robin Atthill (David and Charles 1964).

The site map of Fussells Ironworks on Page 4 is reproduced by kind permission of Mr Robin Stiles and Mr Mike Bone of the Bristol Industrial Archaeological Society.

Our thanks to: Mr David Bromwich (Somerset Studies Library), for his helpful assistance during the preparation of the first edition; Mr John Cornwell, for permission to reproduce photographs from his collection; Mr Jim Coyne, for his cooperation; Mr Charles George of Chantry, for his helpful information during the preparation of the first edition; Ms Ceri Johnson and Mrs Sally Twiss of The National Trust, for their cooperation.

Our acknowledgement to the late Mr Terry Milton, for the use of his library.

"The Paviours", an early nineteenth century engraving by J. Miller. The Fussell edge tool business would have benefited from the improved methods of road construction that were being undertaken in the Somerset area at this time.

Bibliography

Atthill, Robin: *"Old Mendip"*, David & Charles, 1964

Atthill, Robin: *"The Somerset & Dorset Railway"*, David & Charles, 1967 (New Edition 1987)

Barron, Robert Albany: *"The Finch Foundry Trust and Sticklepath Museum of Rural Industry"*, Finch Foundry Trust

Bristol Industrial Archaeological Society: *"Journals"*

Bromwich, David and Dunning, Robert: *"Victorian and Edwardian Somerset from Old Photographs"*, B T Batsford, 1977

Buchanan, Angus and Cossons, Neil: *"Industrial Archaeology of the Bristol Region"*, David and Charles, 1969

Burton, Anthony: *"Remains of a Revolution"*, Andre Deutsch, 1974

Cleverden, Rev John: *"A History of Mells"*, ed Michael McGarvie, 1974

Collinson, Rev John: *"History and Antiquities of Somerset"*, 1791

Harper, Duncan: *"Wilts & Somerset, A Railway Landscape"*, Millstream Books 1987

Opie, Iona and Peter: *"The Oxford Dictionary of Nursery Rhymes"*, Oxford University Press, 1951, (1992 edition used)

Reid, Dr R.D: *"A Water Hammer"*, The Somerset Year Book 1935"

Skinner, John: *"A Journal of a Somerset Rector"* 1803 - 1834", ed. Howard and Peter Coombes, Kingsmead Press 1930 (revised 1971)

Toulson, Shirley: *"The Mendip Hills"*, Victor Gollancz Limited, 1984

Woodward, Llewellyn: *"The Age of Reform 1815 - 1870"*, Oxford University Press 1951 (1992 edition used)

Various publications from the Local Studies sections of Frome and Taunton Libraries

Other titles by FIDUCIA PRESS include:

Tom Lamb
The Organ Grinder £3.00
A verbal Obsession
Manly Monodes £3.00
26 Alliterative poems. An adventure in words by the Scottish Poet

Mark Griffiths
Tracts from the Tracks £2.00
Collected poems

Ernest Clifford Hazell
The Gentle Giants £3.00
Shire horses and the history of a timber haulage family 1880 - 1935

Dave Collett
Dave Collett Blues £5.00
A selection of his words and music

Dennis Spear
Recollections of Chew Magna £5.00
A decade to remember 1930-1940

Dave Hibberd
Recollections of Jazz in Bristol £10.00
A rich slice of musical social history